The Pet

CW00823526

by

Nigel MacLennan

"Very positive! Cleverly written. A gripping read. A book to inspire and act as a catalyst for change, which is also a gripping suspense thriller! Take a little of the surreal cult series 'The Prisoner' and elements of Orwell's '1984', throw in a good helping of Tony Robbins' 'Unlimited Power' and add a big pinch of Napoleon Hill's 'Think and Grow Rich' and you have Nigel MacLennan's 'The Perfect Gift'!

". . . this publication clearly and cleverly emphasises and drives home the message that the ultimate responsibility for achieving one's potential lies within oneself; in one's own belief in, and one's ability to control one's thoughts, behaviours and emotions.

Written almost exclusively in pure dialogue and with some comforting reinforcement and repetition, this is not a book for those 'victims' wishing to use old wounds as excuses, but for those ready and looking to develop more positive thought and action. You should emerge convinced that mind power-removes limitations; you can be all your can be."
Sherridan Hughes, Chartered Psychologist, CareerMax

"The Perfect Gift seems the perfect vehicle for getting across a very powerful message. What will the book do for people? I have no doubt it will open eyes. It is an intriguing, potentially important book, and one that I could easily imagine going back to again and again."
Peter Jackson, Director of Human Resources, T & S Stores Plc

"I highly commend this book to anyone who wants to know the secret of living the life of their dreams. It offers practical lessons which should be made available to everyone setting out on the journey to fulfil their destiny. 'Give a man fish and you feed him for a day. Teach him to fish and you feed him for a lifetime.' This book provides the essential tools for a lifetime of success and happiness."
Robert A. Scott, Managing Director – Change Your Life Ltd

"This is the book I have been waiting for ... The Perfect Gift is awesome!"
Mary Mahon, Physiotherapist, New York

"The message is very powerful, it's absolutely terrific. Lots of people really need this material."
Clive Mason, HR Director in the Atofina Group

"Unusual, easy to read and kept my attention all the way through. I could see this book having a potential audience from schoolchildren to professionals."
Pete Connor, IT Director, Argos Retail Group

"If this book were an LP [CD] it would have the feel of Peter Green, the power of Black Sabbath and the integrity of Harvey Andrews."
Bob MacKay, Freelance Trainer – Graduate retention and action learning

---

"A thought provoking and challenging book. I read it in one sitting. Repeated reads will reward you."
Guy Perry, Media Consultant, Barnes Perry

"The Perfect Gift is a spangling voyage of discovery. Incisive and thought provoking."
Wayne Stackhouse, The Birmingham Mail

"I enjoyed reading it, and am sure it will be a roaring success. I found it interesting and stimulating and enjoyed the suspense leading up to the revelation of The Perfect Gift."
Paul Duncan, HR Director, Jewson

"Not the normal kind of book I would read, but I enjoyed it enormously, twice!"
Peter Pollard, Retired Regimental Sergeant Major, British Army

---

"A very interesting and useful read. Great for people who are facing a major life challenge."
Neil Lawrence, Operations Director, Jewson

"Congratulations on a wonderful piece of writing . . . creative, imaginative and appropriate. The Perfect Gift has a wonderfully exciting title and . . . the story as it evolves continually raises your curiosity . . . it gives a great deal of food for thought."
Bernie Smith, Head Teacher, Four Dwellings School, Birmingham

---

"Better than 'Great Expectations'."
Rob Cleveland, Principal Child Protection Officer, Birmingham Social Services

---

"The principles in this book will enhance any area of your life you choose to apply them to."
Eden Voss, Author and Playwright

"A revelation of a book."
Marcus Steane, Health Care Manager

"Avec 'The Perfect Gift' tout est possible!" (With The Perfect Gift everything is possible.)
Beatrice Baille, French Tutor

The Perfect Gift

Nigel MacLennan

Aria

Published by Aria
Freepost MID25295
Birmingham
B17 9BR
UK

British Library Catalogue in Publication Data Available

ISBN 0–9543658–0–1

Library of Congress Catalogue-in-Publication Data Available

Phototypeset by Intype London Ltd
Printed in Great Britain at the University Press, Cambridge

Cover design by Nigel MacLennan
Cover graphics by Chris Manley, Codsall, Wolverhampton

Dedication

The Perfect Gift is dedicated to everyone who has not yet found it, to those whose lives would be profoundly changed by it, to those who don't even know of its existence and to those who know of its existence and actively resist it to their detriment.

Contents

Acknowledgements

What you hold in your hand is the result of input and suggestions by many people. Some of them my teachers officially, many more of them my teachers unofficially.

Specifically my thanks go to the many people I have had the privilege to coach over the years for repeatedly telling me how powerful they found my simple models to be. To those who challenged me to make my work more accessible to the wider public and not just the business elite, thank you, you were right.

To the many companies whose Boards I have had the privilege to lead, thankyou. Your incisive observations have helped me to refine my material.

To all the people who read the first draft of this book and made constructive suggestions for improvement, thankyou. You are: Bob Mackay, Sherridan Hughes, Bob Scott, Peter Jackson, Bernie Smith, Guy Perry, Wayne Stackhouse, Bob Cleveland, Pete Connor, Neil Lawrence, Peter Pollard, Paul Duncan, Clive Mason, Mary Mahon, Marcus Steane, Eden Voss and Beatrice Baille.

To a very special person whose lifetime service to his country is greatly appreciated by all who love the freedom he protected for so long, even if they don't know him. But I know him and have this opportunity to thank him for being such an outstanding father to me for the last 15 years, and for making my mother so happy. Peter Pollard, thankyou, immensely.

To my mother who overcame obstacle after obstacle over 18 years and more, who showed me by practising much of what has found its way into my books, and who made it possible for me to contribute to the lives of so many, you gave The Perfect Gift, thankyou.

Chapter 1

The invitation

"Why do they want to see *me*?" thought a concerned Apprentice of Life to herself. "Perhaps my coming of age has something to do with it. They said that everyone at my age receives this honour. What honour? *'Receive*?' It feels more like an ordeal than a gift, and who are *they*?" her concerns continued.

Sitting together, the Custodians of The Perfect Gift speculated out loud about which option their latest Apprentice would choose. Passing time drew their idle speculation closer to the point of resolution. "It is time," asserted the Chair for this meeting. The Chair of the Custodians was the youngest Chair of Custodians ever elected. An honour indeed, since he had only received The Perfect Gift himself two years previously.

"Has she arrived yet?"

"Yes Chair, she has just arrived," replied the Senior Custodian, "but she is very nervous."

"Please ask the Apprentice of Life to come in," commanded the Chair of the Custodians in his official capacity. " Senior Custodian, could you introduce yourself to her, put her at ease and tell her about the

1

wonderful choice that awaits her. Could you sit with her throughout the proceedings and give her any guidance you think she might need," added the Chair of the Custodians with the memories of how unjustifiably nervous he had been still fresh in his mind.

"Hello, Apprentice of Life, I am The Senior Custodian."

"Hi, Senior Custodian . . . Why do you call me Apprentice of Life? Why do you use your title instead of your name?" replied the Apprentice with a friendly tone at first and then a touch of concerned curiosity.

"You are as intelligent and questioning as I thought you would be. Here you are about to take the biggest decision of your life and your first thought is to learn."

"What do you mean I am about to take the biggest decision of my life? How do you know whether I am intelligent or not?" quizzed the Apprentice with a much higher pitched and defensive tone.

"What you are about to receive is The Perfect Gift for you. You are going to be given several choices. Choices that I too made a few years ago. You have nothing to fear. In fact you have every reason to celebrate. Not every society gives its young the opportunity to have The Perfect Gift at such a young age. At the end of this meeting you will be very pleased at what you have been offered. Nothing but good will come of this meeting. Are you willing to trust me to help you through the meeting?"

"Y . . . e . . . sssss," replied the Apprentice hesitantly.

The Senior Custodian opened the door and they walked into the adjoining room.

"Apprentice of Life, here are the people who are going to give you The Perfect Gift," announced the Senior Custodian. "Please, sit here with me."

The Apprentice did as she was asked, but was still concerned.

"Can you tell me why you have asked me here?"

"To give you a gift, The Perfect Gift," said the Chair of the Custodians in a tone that conveyed a wisdom and kindness of a man three times his age. "To give you the best opportunity any human being can ever have."

"Why only me?"

"You are at the age where The Perfect Gift is rightfully yours," answered the Chair of the Custodians. "Everyone at your age receives the choices you are about to receive."

"Why have I not been told about this before? Why have my older friends not told me about this?"

"Yes, you're right, your friends have had the opportunity to choose The Perfect Gift, and we are pleased to hear that they have not told you about it. They have kept their oath of secrecy. Your friends are honourable, and you should consider yourself fortunate to have such trustworthy friends." The Chair of the Custodians had become a master of tact and diplomacy at an age when most young men are still battling with their aggressive urges.

"Honourable friends . . . Very fortunate," echoed the other Custodians.

"You too will be asked to swear an oath of secrecy at the end of your choice, and that oath will be a condition of you receiving your Perfect Gift. Do you want to continue?" asked the Chair of the Custodians letting the Apprentice of Life know that she had control; that she could leave if she wanted to.

"Yes, and thankyou all for giving me this opportunity, but what is . . ."

"It is our pleasure to serve," said the Chair of the Custodians interrupting a question that could wait.

He continued: "You are about to make your own life, make your own career, and probably make your own family, eventually. You are here today to choose what assistance, what gift you would like us to give you in making your own life."

All of the Custodians noticed the tension visibly leave the Apprentice of Life.

She knew she was in good hands and knew that those who, only a few minutes ago, had seemed so distant, official and intimidating were none of those things.

Chapter 2

The Choice

"There are many things we could do to help you," began the Chair of the Custodians, "you could have assistance with the purchase of material things – a home or transport. You could have assistance with your career in the form of more education, or in the form of us giving you introductions to people who can help your career. You can even have assistance with your hobbies, in the form of equipment or training or contacts. Or, you can have The Perfect Gift . . ." the Chair of the Custodians left a dramatic pause. ". . . You must make your choice by this time tomorrow. Once you have decided we will do everything required to give you what you have chosen."

"Thank you so much . . ." replied the composed and grateful Apprentice. ". . . Ah . . . I think I'm going to need some help. Can you tell me more about what each option involves, what are the rules?"

"You can choose only one thing. The financial value of each choice is identical. You will have started doing or having what you have chosen within one month," explained the Chair of the Custodians. "And finally, you can discuss this with no one. Not your friends, not your family, no one. If you breach this condition the offer of the Choice will be withdrawn. This is your choice and must not be influenced by anyone else. Do you agree to the terms?"

"Yes. I understand or can figure out each of the options except The Perfect Gift. What is The Perfect Gift?" asked the Apprentice with genuine concern and curiosity. "I couldn't choose . . ."

". . . A gift when you don't know what it is," interrupted the Chair of the Custodians to reassure the Apprentice that the Custodians understood her.

She nodded.

"The Perfect Gift will give you everything you need, either directly or indirectly."

"What is it? How can I . . ." demanded the Apprentice getting impatient at not getting a straight answer, stopping when she felt her hand being squeezed under the table by the Senior Custodian in a calming and reassuring gesture.

"You would like me to explain what it is. Everyone here has chosen The Perfect Gift. The happiest and most successful people have all chosen The Perfect Gift. Some of them know that they have chosen it, most do not. We cannot explain it to you easily or quickly because it is not easy to understand just how much it will do for you."

"Your Senior Custodian told me she thought I was intelligent. I could understand it," said the Apprentice trying another tack.

"You are indeed intelligent; your records confirm that, but accepting The Perfect Gift and using it successfully is made more difficult by the presence of intelligence. Each of us argued and resisted The Perfect Gift for many days before we accepted it. When we stopped resisting and started accepting, it gave us everything, absolutely everything each of us wanted." The Chair of the Custodians paused to give the Apprentice time to reflect.

"If I were to tell you what it is you would probably behave as we did, and you would resist The Perfect Gift before you had even chosen it. You would not choose it. But this I promise you. The Perfect Gift is called that for very good reasons. It will give you everything you want. Everything." Another pause was required.

"Despite being told exactly what you have just been told, very few people choose The Perfect Gift, most choose something other than The Perfect Gift. More than this I cannot tell you. You must choose what gift you would like us to give you. It must be your choice, and yours alone." The Chair of the Custodian's began to conclude his duties. "Will you meet us tomorrow at the same time to give us your decision?"

"How do I decide?" uttered the Apprentice still deep in thought. "Uhhm . . . yes. Thankyou again for giving me this wonderful opportunity."

"Come with me," said the Senior Custodian as she began to lead the Apprentice to the door.

The next day the question on the lips of the Custodians as they waited for the Apprentice to be led in by the Senior Custodian was: "What will she choose?"

The Chair of Custodians asked: "Have you made your decision, Apprentice?"

"Yes, I have. I think that I may be making a mistake. My head tells me to ask for help with material things. Then I will have some kind of security. But my heart tells me you have something very special in this thing you call The Perfect Gift. So I will choose The Perfect Gift."

"Congratulations!" enthused every Custodian in the room simultaneously and spontaneously.

When the noises of support quietened the Chair of the Custodians had a very serious duty to perform. "You have made the best choice, but I can tell that you fear that you have made the worst. My words of reassurance will count for nothing, so I will offer no more. Now I must spring two conditions upon you.

"To be given The Perfect Gift you must agree to become a Custodian if you are asked, and you must be prepared to contribute to the funds that will be used to benefit future generations of Apprentices of Life. The amount of your contribution will be equivalent to the contribution you are about to receive."

"What? Why did you not tell me of these conditions before I made my choice?" quizzed the Apprentice becoming suspicious at the possibility of even more conditions and demands.

"Your choice would have been influenced if you knew you would have had to pay back what you were to be given. It may even have been influenced by the possibility of status as a Custodian, now that you know we exist and what we do. But you made your decision without the interference of those factors," reassured the Chair of the Custodians despite his previous words. "Do you accept that we could not tell you about the conditions before you made your choice?"

"Yes, that seems reasonable."

"Do you agree to the conditions?"

"Yes, I do."

"Thank you for giving us the honour of helping you," said the Chair of the Custodians. "The Senior Custodian will now brief you on how you will receive The Perfect Gift."

"It feels odd that you are thanking me!" exclaimed the Apprentice. "Surely I'm the one who should be grateful."

The Apprentice and her guide moved out of the room.

"OK," began the Senior Custodian, "shall we do the briefing?"

As the Senior Custodian conducted the briefing outside the room, the other Custodians inside finalised their part in the programme for the Apprentice.

After the briefing the Senior Custodian again took the Apprentice's hand, squeezed it and said: "You have a wonderful journey ahead of you; go home and rest. Empty your mind of all things before your first meeting."

Chapter 3

The First Custodian

"Come in," heard the Apprentice after knocking the door.

She opened the door and stopped when she saw who it was. The Chair of Custodians saw her reaction and immediately sought to calm and reassure the Apprentice. "I'm so pleased to be the first person on your schedule. Please come in and make yourself comfortable."

"I was not expecting to see you," replied the Apprentice, "the schedule just gave me addresses and times."

"Yes, that is to prevent you second guessing what will happen and preparing yourself. We've found over the years that Apprentices learn fastest when they are most open minded."

"It worked; I have no idea why I am here or what is going to happen." This time it was the Apprentice who was providing the reassurance.

"Let's have a chat about life. Specifically about behaviour," said the Chair of the Custodians. "Tell me, what causes you to behave in any particular way?"

"Circumstances," quickly asserted the Apprentice.

The Chair of the Custodians nodded and looked encouragingly into the eyes of the Apprentice.

"My behaviour comes directly from what is happening around me."

The Chair of the Custodians repeated his previous silent response.

"If my friends have a problem, I do whatever I can to help them. The circumstances cause my behaviour."

"If your friends asked you to commit a serious crime to help them solve a non-life threatening problem would you do it?" calmly asked the Chair of the Custodians.

"Of course not!"

"What's the difference between helping your friends normally and helping them if they want you to commit a crime?" said the Chair with a tone that would calm the seas.

"I would never commit a crime unless I absolutely had to," replied the Apprentice with a question in her voice.

"When you say 'had to' what do you mean?"

"I mean committing the crime was the only choice."

"Tell me what group of people would say exactly what you've just said," requested the Chair of the Custodians.

"I don't know."

"Criminals. The population of our prisons," said the Chair of the Custodians. "Many of them say that they had no choice. Is it true that all the people that we send to prison truly had no choice in their behaviour?"

"No, of course not. They did have choices. They chose not to take the alternatives," insisted the Apprentice.

"So they had alternatives?"

"Yes," immediately replied the Apprentice.

"Are there always alternatives?" continued the Chair of the Custodians, "Do you ever have to commit a crime?"

"The alternatives might be limited, but yes there are always alternatives."

"And looking outside the world of criminals, do law abiding citizens have choices in the way they behave?" asked the Chair of the Custodians.

"Sometimes there is only one option."

"So, criminals have the choice of alternative behaviours but law abiding people do not, do you think that is right?" asked the Chair of the Custodians.

"I suppose not, but this doesn't feel right. You seem to be using your experience to out argue me."

Avoiding the confrontation that may have followed by responding to the Apprentice's assertion, the Chair of the Custodians simply asked: "Who is responsible for your behaviour, you or I?"

"I am, but you can influence my behaviour."

"Can you choose how you respond to my attempts to influence your behaviour?"

"Of course," replied the Apprentice.

"So, who is responsible for your behaviour, you or I?" repeated the Chair of the Custodians.

"I am," agreed the Apprentice of Life reluctantly.

"Are you always responsible for your behaviour?" continued the Chair of the Custodians.

"Always is a lot of possibilities; I don't know if I can think of every possibility and I would need to do that to answer your question. Without doing that, I don't know."

"Gosh, you are indeed intelligent," observed the Chair of the Custodians. "Perhaps you could give me an example of when you are not responsible for your behaviour?"

There was a long silence, during which the Chair of the Custodians looked on with calm and supportive body language.

"You're right. I am always responsible for my behaviour. Except if there was something outside controlling me, like extreme hunger or epilepsy." The Apprentice was close to the end of her first meeting, but didn't know it yet.

"Epilepsy, yes I agree, your behaviour during an episode is outside your control, but how you deal with the disorder before and after is totally within your control. We all know people who deal with epilepsy with dignity.

"Hunger . . . Let me pose a question. Has anyone ever deliberately starved themselves to death?" asked the Chair of the Custodians with a humility that reassured the Apprentice that she was not going to be emotionally abused.

"Yes, people have starved themselves to death as a

protest," she paused for a long time. "I suppose that means that I could overrule even things like hunger to control my behaviour."

"Yes, you can. You already can. You have control over your behaviour," the Chair of the Custodian paused. "You have already taken the first step to acquiring The Perfect Gift." said the Chair of the Custodians beginning to wrap up the session.

"Hold on. I agree that I can, in theory, control my behaviour, but I haven't controlled it in the past, even when I've tried! I mean really, really tried. I've told myself that I'm going to do, or not do something, and I've really meant it and then I've broken my promise to myself. I feel really bad about myself when that happens and that has happened more times than I'd like to admit," protested the Apprentice of Life.

"Each word you say confirms that you have made the right choice, each word you say confirms that you want what The Perfect Gift will give you, each word you say confirms that you will benefit immensely from The Perfect Gift," said the Chair of the Custodians using his best rhetoric.

The hairs on the back of the Apprentice's neck stood on end. She struggled to compose herself. "If . . . if . . . if . . . I have control over my behaviour, why, ehm, why don't I have control over my behaviour?"

"That question will be answered and you will learn how to control your behaviour as part of being given The Perfect Gift. But our time together is over. You should go home and sleep before going to your next appointment. Before you go, let me say again how honoured I am to have served you thus far."

"Why do you keep saying that you are honoured to help me?" asked the Apprentice still confused by the apparent role reversal of the thanks offered by the Custodians.

"When you have The Perfect Gift you will know." The Chair of the Custodians showed the Apprentice to the door.

On her way home the Apprentice could not help but dwell on the lesson she had just learned. "OK, so I have control of my behaviour in theory, but why can't I do it in practice? What is this Perfect Gift? Why don't or won't they use their real names? Why use these quaint titles? Why all this continual thanksgiving when it is they who claim to be helping me?" The thoughts continued all the way through the night, jumping around inside her head as if they had a life of their own.

Chapter 4

The Second Custodian

"Come in," said the Second Custodian.

The Apprentice entered the room, less nervous than last time, in fact, totally calm. "Why should I be so calm?" she thought as she made friendly eye contact with the woman who had squeezed her hand in reassurance only a few days ago. "Hello, Senior Custodian, it is nice to see you again."

"We have a lot to do today. Can you carry that portable music centre and follow me?" gently commanded the Senior Custodian as she gestured to the little blue music centre with two sets of earphones attached to it.

Complying, the Apprentice picked up the portable kit and followed the Senior Custodian through the door.

"Where are we going?" asked the Apprentice.

"On a journey short in the world and long in the mind," replied the Senior Custodian enigmatically. "It will all become clear."

They walked to a hospital. "Put on a headset," instructed the Senior Custodian while putting one on herself.

As they walked into a children's play area within

the hospital grounds the music playing through the earphones was sad and sombre.

Starting to feel uneasy the Apprentice of Life said: "This sounds like a funeral march."

"It is. Everyone of these children is terminally ill," said the Senior Custodian in a voice so filled with sadness that the tone alone brought tears to the eyes of the Apprentice.

The haunting melody of the music combined with the images of dying children trying to play in the sun, despite their devastating illnesses, brought a profound sense of helpless grief to the Apprentice. As a cascade of tears ran down her face the Apprentice expected some support from the Senior Custodian, but it did not come. Instead the Senior Custodian signalled the Apprentice to follow her.

As they were walking the Senior Custodian changed the music. This time it was upbeat inspirational music. Music similar in feel to happy gospel songs.

Just as the Apprentice was enjoying the music they walked into the visiting area of a maternity ward. Everywhere there were tired, but smiling mothers with radiant babies, fathers glowing with pride, brothers and sisters amazed and engrossed by the new addition to their families. There were bright colours and interesting shapes.

"This is fantastic," thought the Apprentice just as she realised how great she felt.

Seeing the glow on her face the Senior Custodian

knew it was time for the next part of the journey. She signalled the Apprentice to follow.

"Why is she taking me to all these places?" wondered the Apprentice. "What is she trying to do? And why all this music? What's going on?"

Again, as they walked, the Senior Custodian changed the music. This time the music was peaceful, calm, reassuring. The kind that made the Apprentice feel instantly relaxed. She no longer needed to know; it didn't matter why the Senior Custodian was taking her on this musical journey.

Then they turned a corner into the entrance of a graveyard. The Apprentice hated graveyards. Everytime she had been to one it was after losing an elderly loved one.

The Senior Custodian led the Apprentice to a series of gravestones and asked the Apprentice to read them. Each was of a young person cut down before they had even had the chance to reach the prime of their lives. Normally such a thing would have brought the Apprentice to tears, yet somehow she felt only peace.

"Let's move on, I have one more thing to show you," said the Senior Custodian gesturing to a waiting car. When they got in, the driver was none other than the Chair of the Custodians. He nodded gracefully to his two passengers and immediately the doors were closed, drove without saying a word.

"Where are we going?" asked the Apprentice.

"When we get there I want you to put on this helmet,"

said the Senior Custodian passing the Apprentice a motor sports safety helmet.

"It has speakers inside it," stated the Apprentice in surprise as she inspected it. "You're going to have me drive around the racetrack listening to music," exclaimed the Apprentice as she realised that the Custodians obviously knew that her hobby was karting.

When they arrived at the circuit no one else was around, except the safety staff.

"You know what to do," reassured the Senior Custodian. "I'll be in the canteen when you have finished."

The Apprentice put on the helmet. It was playing the same calming music that she had heard at the graveyard. "It seems to be having an effect on my driving; the lap time display has me up half a second on my record for this circuit." Just then the music changed. It was the harsh, very loud and disjointed music that a few of her friends had said that they liked. "How could anybody like that?" she thought just as she noticed that her lap times had dropped by a full second. "No, that can't be. I didn't make any mistakes," she protested to herself. "I must try harder."

"What? I'm still down. This awful music, I've got to stop it! What? No! I don't believe it. She's turning up the volume! It's way too loud!"

When she came to a screeching stop in the pits the Apprentice ripped the helmet off her head, hurting her ears in the process. "What the hell is going on?" she raged to herself.

Walking aggressively to the canteen her anger built.

"Why did you turn up that awful music to deafening levels? You knew there was no way I could stop it while driving at speed with my helmet on. Are you trying to damage my hearing? Why the trip to these locations? Why the music?" she demanded of the Senior Custodian.

"I'm not going to tell you," said the Senior Custodian, as she sipped her drink and continued reading her newspapers.

"What do you mean you're not going to tell me?" demanded the Apprentice.

The Senior Custodian said nothing and continued as if she hadn't heard the Apprentice.

"What do you mean you're not going to tell me?" repeated the Apprentice with increasing levels of anger in her voice.

"Do you want to know?" asked the Senior Custodian with an air of utter indifference.

"Yes, I wouldn't have asked if I didn't!" barked the Apprentice.

"How do you feel right now?" asked the Senior Custodian as if asking someone to pass the sugar bowl.

"Why are you asking me how I feel? I want to know why all these games." The Apprentice's anger was now in full flow.

"If you tell me how you feel, I can begin to answer your question."

"OK, I'm angry. I'm angry that you won't tell me

what's going on. That you played that horrible music that spoiled my lap times. That you repeatedly made it louder until it was unbearable. That you seem totally indifferent to my requests," bellowed the Apprentice.

"Good," calmly said the Senior Custodian.

The Apprentice was now so incensed that she couldn't speak. That was probably just as well for what she wanted to say would have not been good for her relationship with the Senior Custodian.

"Please sit down. I have something for you that is extremely valuable. Here, I've even brought along your favourite drink," charmed the Senior Custodian as she passed the drink.

In that same reassuring tone used by the Chair of the Custodians the Senior Custodian then asked: "Who is responsible for your behaviour?"

"I am," said the Apprentice calming a little.

"If what the Chair of the Custodians told me is correct, you want to know what makes it difficult to control your behaviour and how you can actually control it, is that right?"

"Yes, that's right," the Apprentice grunted in reluctant agreement.

"OK, then let us recap on what you have experienced today. When you saw the dying children trying to play, while listening to that profoundly sad music, how did you feel?"

"I'm sure you can imagine," said the Apprentice just starting to calm down, and just starting to realise that what had happened today was to show her something of immense value, and that the Custodians had gone to considerable lengths to set it all up for her.

"I felt the deepest sadness I can remember apart from when I've lost a loved one . . . I'm sorry I was angry with you; I am grateful for what you are trying to do, even though I'm not quite sure what that is. Please accept my apologies."

"It may help you to know that I reacted exactly as you did when I was being given The Perfect Gift," assured the Senior Custodian. "How did you feel in the visiting area of the maternity ward?"

"Full of hope and joy and happiness, and maybe a touch of anticipation for when I have the privilege of creating new life."

"You are indeed wise beyond your years. In the grave-yard, how did you feel?" asked the Senior Custodian encouragingly.

"I've never felt so peaceful, and to feel like that in a place I would normally associate with grief and sadness, a place I would rather not go . . . It was strangely OK . . . I can't describe it better than that."

"And we already know how you felt here. You described that exceptionally well!" mused the Senior Custodian.

They both laughed as the remainder of the tension subsided.

"What caused you to feel so differently in the different

locations in such a short period of time?" asked the Senior Custodian in that especially safe tone of voice.

"The music combined with where I was and what I was seeing," asserted the Apprentice getting a sense of the fact that the last time she made such an assertion a major lesson was just around the corner.

"Was the music responsible for how you felt? The circumstances you find yourself in, are they responsible for what you feel?" asked the Senior Custodian in a totally neutral voice.

"Yes, exactly."

"OK, I want you to tell me about the happiest time of your life. Describe it in as much detail as possible."

The Apprentice did so.

"How do you feel right now?" asked the Senior Custodian.

"Fantastic," replied the Apprentice in a tone of extreme joy.

"OK, I want you to tell me about the most unhappy time of your life. Describe it in as much detail as possible."

The Apprentice did so.

"How do you feel right now?" asked the Senior Custodian.

"Terrible," replied the Apprentice slowly and heavily.

"You have just gone from feeling fantastic to feeling lousy in a few minutes. There was no music, you were sat right here all along, your circumstances did not change. Do you agree?"

"Yes, I suppose so," conceded the Apprentice.

"So what *was* responsible for how you felt?" Asked the Senior Custodian in that magic 'you know you'll be safe answering anything I ask you' voice.

"The things you asked me to describe. They caused my feelings."

"And if you had asked yourself those same questions who would have been responsible for the way you felt?" asked the Senior Custodian.

"I suppose I would have been," replied the Apprentice hesitantly.

"And if you had planned the music and the journey we took today who would have been responsible for how you felt?"

"Again, I would," replied the Apprentice of Life with a little more certainty.

"And if I now tried to deliberately provoke you to anger in the way I did previously, would I succeed?" continued the Senior Custodian with her helpful leading questions.

"I hope not. No."

"And how would you manage that?" asked the Senior Custodian.

"I would just refuse to be provoked," replied the Apprentice of Life.

"You mean by controlling your feelings?" asked the Senior Custodian again using that magically reassuring voice.

"Yes."

"So, who is responsible for controlling the way you feel?" asked the Senior Custodian again using that magical voice.

Half challenging and half conceding, the Apprentice said: "I suppose I am, but I find that hard to stomach. Even if I am responsible for how I feel, how do I control it?"

"That question you will have answered in your next meeting, but there is one more thing you will benefit from before then.

"What is the connection between how you behave and how you feel?" asked the Senior Custodian.

"Uh . . . Ehm . . . I don't know."

"Yes you do. When you were feeling angry how did you behave?" challenged the Senior Custodian.

"Like an angry person. My voice was raised, in pitch and volume; my gestures were aggressive."

"And when you were behaving like a person in grief at the children's play area, how did you feel?" continued the Senior Custodian.

"Deeply sad."

"What is the connection between how you behave and how you feel?" repeated the Senior Custodian.

"How I feel influences the way I behave."

"Is that true the other way round?" asked the Senior Custodian.

"You mean, do I feel a particular way because of how I behave?"

"Yes," replied the Senior Custodian.

"Yes. I suppose that is true as well."

"Excellent, we have reached the end of our discussion. Before you have your next meeting I'd like you to come up with a written summary of what you have learned from your meetings. Now let's get you home," said the Senior Custodian as she motioned towards the waiting car.

"But I still don't understand how to control how I feel or how I behave?" challenged the Apprentice.

"Be patient. You have another meeting tomorrow."

When she arrived home the Apprentice of Life wrote in her diary:

I am in control of my behaviour.

I am in control of my feelings.

What I feel controls how I behave.

How I behave feeds back to influence how I feel.

But, I don't understand how to control my behaviour or my feelings.

Chapter 5

The Third Custodian

The following day it took the Apprentice several hours to reach her next appointment. She had wondered why it had been set for midday. Now she knew. As she approached the farm she scanned the cluster of buildings wondering where she should go and for whom she should ask. "What were the Custodians playing at; sending her to a meeting on a large farm so far away and with no contact name?" thought the Apprentice.

The roaring of a huge tractor came from behind her. She moved to let it pass. It stopped alongside her.

"Jump in." said the farmer with a beaming smile on his face.

"How do I . . ." started the Apprentice as the farmer lent down to offer a helping hand.

Once in the tractor's cab the farmer said: "You must be the Apprentice of Life. It is an honour to have you come to my farm, and even more of an honour to be the Custodian helping you with your third meeting. How have your other meetings gone?"

"Hmm, well although I really enjoyed the company I

don't think I understand what is going on or what The Perfect Gift is. In fact, I'm quite confused."

"In that case, you are progressing according to plan!" reassured the Third Custodian.

"Well, thankyou. I don't suppose there is any point in asking you either what the plan is or what progress I am supposed to be making?"

"Ha, ha, ha," boomed the Third Custodian, "You are as sharp as my colleagues said you are."

When the tractor came to a stop in the courtyard of the farmhouse the Third Custodian got out and helped the Apprentice down.

"It's feeding time. Will you help me feed the animals?"

"I don't know anything about farm animals, but if you show me what to do, yes."

They began to walk over to a feeding trough at the side of an enclosed area, half inside and half covered.

"Watch what happens as I walk up to the trough," said the Third Custodian.

Most of the animals came to gather around the trough.

"They know that you are going to feed them," said the Apprentice.

"How do you think they feel right now?" asked the Third Custodian.

"Hungry," replied the Apprentice.

"Hungry and?" returned the Third Custodian.

"Hungry and perhaps anticipating that you are going to feed them."

"How are they behaving?" continued the Third Custodian.

"They are jostling for position around the trough."

"If you were sure that they could think, what would you say most of them are thinking now?" asked the Third Custodian in that same magical tone of voice used by all the other Custodians.

"They're probably thinking 'Come on – FEED ME!' " joked the Apprentice.

"There was I thinking that I ran this farm, and here I am being told what to do by a bunch of animals," joked the Third Custodian in turn.

They both smiled.

"What triggered the behaviour you see right now?" asked the Third Custodian.

"You walked towards the trough."

"What happened after that?" asked the Third Custodian.

"The animals moved towards the trough," replied the Apprentice.

"Yes, that's true. But what happened inside the animals *after* they saw me walking towards the trough and *before* they did the same?" asked the Third Custodian trying a more precise question.

"They must have 'thought' . . ." the Apprentice paused, knowing she was on shaky ground, ". . . that you going towards the trough meant food for them."

"Absolutely right. How did they feel after they had

that thought?" asked the Third Custodian sensing that the Apprentice was close.

"I'm uncomfortable with this. We don't know if animals can 'think' or 'feel' in the sense we do," replied the Apprentice making the Third Custodian aware that a little more work was required.

"Agreed. Just indulge me for a moment. Assume that animals can think and feel in some way. If they can, how do you think they felt after they had that thought 'farmer at trough means food for me, now'?"

"Excited. Full of anticipation. Anxious to get a good spot at the trough," indulged the Apprentice.

"Now tell me, what was the sequence of events in the chain we have just described?" continued the Third Custodian.

"You walked towards the trough, the animals 'thought' that food was likely to follow, they became excited at that prospect, then their behaviour changed from what they were previously doing to moving towards the trough and jostling for position," asserted the Apprentice, but this time she knew she was right.

"I believe you know that is right," asserted the Third Custodian reading the Apprentices body language. "Now let's apply your chain of events to human beings. In fact, let's apply it to you.

"When you went on the musical journey yesterday. How did you feel just before the tears flowed down your face at the children's play area?" the Third Custodian paused. "... I spoke with the Second Custodian last night."

"Extremely sad. Helpless."

"What were you thinking just before you felt like that?" asked the Third Custodian.

"How desperately the children wanted to play. How despite their devastating illnesses they were determined to play." The thoughts were again making the Apprentice highly emotional.

Her eyes welled up again.

"Why are your eyes filled with tears?" asked the Third Custodian.

"Because I'm thinking about these poor children and it is making me ..."

A look of realisation spread across the face of the Apprentice.

"What I think determines what I feel and what I feel determines how I behave!"

The Third Custodian smiled and nodded his head.

"If you want to control how you behave, what do you have to control?" asked the Third Custodian.

"How I feel," enthused the Apprentice.

"If you want to control how you feel, what do you have to control?" asked the Third Custodian.

"What I think about." The Apprentice could barely contain her enthusiasm yet only thirty seconds ago she had been on the verge of tears.

"Going back to what you said to the First Custodian, why can you not get yourself to stick to some of the behaviours you have planned? And why can you not avoid some of the behaviours you don't want to enact?" the Third Custodian asked, aware that the mood would again change instantly with his question.

"Because I'm not thinking in a way that is going to give me the behaviour I want..." the Apprentice paused. Her face lost its glow. "No! When I am trying to get myself to do something or not do something I do actually think 'I must, I must, I must do this,' and still I don't, still I can't get myself to do it, or *not* do it as the case may be. Why is that?" self-quizzed the Apprentice thinking out loud in front of the Third Custodian.

The Third Custodian gestured to the Apprentice to continue.

"What I think doesn't change anything," said the Apprentice defiantly.

"Did thinking change the way you felt about 30 seconds ago when you were thinking about the children again?" asked the Third Custodian.

"Yes, it did, but my thinking does not help my inability to behave in ways I want to or stop me behaving in ways I don't want to."

"When have you been able to control your behaviour?" asked the Third Custodian.

"Most times I can, but when I can't it causes me great difficulty," replied the Apprentice.

"What do you think is the difference between the occasions when you can control your behaviour and those when you can't?" asked the Third Custodian.

"I don't know ... is there more to controlling my behaviour than just thinking?"

"Completely right! It has been a pleasure to help you." glowed the Third Custodian.

"What do you mean ...?" the Apprentice paused. "What do you mean I'm completely right; I was just making a guess. I don't understand why you think my guess is right. What does it mean that there is more to controlling behaviour than just thinking?" asked the perplexed and annoyed Apprentice.

"It means that you now know what you don't know. You know that there is more to controlling behaviour than thinking. You now know what you need to know. You need to know what it is, in addition to thinking and feeling, that controls your behaviour. Do you agree?" clarified the Third Custodian.

"Yes, I do ... Are you also telling me that our meeting is over?" asked the frustrated Apprentice.

"Let me take you to your pick up point. And please, accept my thanks for giving me the opportunity to help you on your way to obtaining The Perfect Gift," said the Third Custodian with total sincerity as he pointed towards the tractor.

"Promise me that you will write some notes to sum-marise what you have learned today," requested the Third Custodian as he dropped the Apprentice at her pick up point.

"I promise. Thank you, very much, for your patience with me."

"It was my honour," concluded the Third Custodian.

While on her way home the Apprentice wrote in her diary:

I am in control of my behaviour.

I am in control of my feelings.

What I feel controls how I behave.

How I behave feeds back to influence how I feel.

What I think influences what I feel and therefore how I behave.

But what controls what I think?

Chapter 6

The Fourth Custodian

"A theatre! Why have they sent me to a theatre?" thought the Apprentice as she realised that the address to which she was sent was not an office as she had expected.

She walked into the reception area adjoining the box office. No one was around. She looked for a bell or an office door. She could find neither. "Hello?"

Silence.

"HELLO!"

Still nothing. She looked around for a seat while thinking: "Whomever I'm supposed to meet must be late. No seats. Perhaps someone has left a message. Where would you leave a message here? Ah, yes, the box office."

The Apprentice walked over to the box office. "I knew it," she thought.

There was a note: 'I've had to go out for two minutes, please open the door and take a seat in the box office until I return. Thanks.'

"That was thoughtful," reflected the Apprentice as she took a seat.

The Apprentice was looking around when a young man with facial disfigurement rushed into the theatre.

As the young man was frantically looking around the Apprentice thought: "That's not disfigurement, it's a mask! He's carrying a *gun*! Oh no . . . He's seen me. He's pointing the gun at me. He is coming towards me." She could feel herself reaching a state of terror.

"If you don't give me what I want I will kill you. Do you understand? Now give me the money!"

"I don't work he . . ." The young man shoved the gun in the Apprentice's throat, cutting her off immediately.

"IF YOU DON'T GIVE ME THE MONEY I'LL KILL YOU. DO YOU UNDERSTAND?"

There was no doubt, this young man meant exactly as he said and the Apprentice knew that he would kill her without the slightest hesitation or regret.

"Ye . . . sss," croaked the Apprentice down the barrel of the gun. "I can't give him anything, I don't work here. He's going to kill me. I'm going to die and there is nothing I can do to stop it. I think I'm going to pass out," she thought as she gradually felt herself going cold and weak.

Lowering the gun and taking off his mask, the young man, instantly turning into a middle aged man, said with that unmistakably reassuring voice: "Hello Apprentice, I am the Fourth Custodian, welcome to your fourth meeting."

Her jaw dropped, then it closed and tightened. "WHAT DO YOU THINK YOU ARE DOING? I COULD

HAVE DIED OF FRIGHT! HOW DARE YOU TREAT ME LIKE THIS!"

"Your thoughts control your feelings, perhaps you can use them to calm yourself," said the Fourth Custodian deliberately provoking the Apprentice.

"THAT'S IT! I'M GOING!" raged the Apprentice as she flew through the door, out of the theatre, down the steps and into the street.

"Apprentice", said the Senior Custodian softly catching the Apprentice's arm, "listen to what I have to offer you." She paused until she could see the look of recognition in the Apprentice's eyes. "What you have just experienced will be of immense value to you. It is taking you very close to The Perfect Gift. If you can just be patient a little longer the gift will be yours." The Senior Custodian's voice was so calming, and her touch, as it had been twice before, was so warm and caring that the Apprentice had become quite calm by the time she knew that she should reply.

"Why are you here? How did you know that I . . .?" trailed off the Apprentice when she realised that everything the Custodians had done so far had been planned, down to the smallest detail. "Thanks. I let my emotions control my behaviour, didn't I?"

"As we all do until we obtain The Perfect Gift", reassured the Senior Custodian, "but . . . letting your emotions control you is a good thing as long as you . . ." she broke off. "Don't let me spoil what you are about to discover," said the Senior Custodian as she recovered.

The Apprentice got a sense that she had just witnessed the first mistake she had experienced from the Custodians. "Who are these 'Custodians'? Why this air of conspiracy for good?" the Apprentice thought.

"The Fourth Custodian is ready to help you to obtain The Perfect Gift," said the Senior Custodian.

Gently touching the Senior Custodian's hand, the Apprentice pulled away and re-entered the theatre. The Fourth Custodian greeted the Apprentice with a 'hands up, look no weapons' gesture, which was only just broader than his smile.

"Why did you think you were about to pass out?" asked the Fourth Custodian getting straight down to business.

"How do you know I thought I was going to pass out?" asked the Apprentice with considerable surprise.

"Your face lost all its colour and your eyes glazed over," replied the Fourth Custodian before repeating: "Why did you think you were about to pass out?"

"I thought I was going to be killed," replied the Apprentice indignantly.

"I know this will sound odd, but what made you think that?" asked the Fourth Custodian extremely aware of the bizarre nature of his question.

"The fact that you . . . the young man with the mask you were playing, had a gun, which he was pressing into my throat, and the fact that he said, 'unless I gave him what he wanted' I would die. I knew I could give him nothing. You set this up so I could give him nothing," protested the Apprentice.

"Was it the circumstances that controlled your thoughts, that controlled your behaviours, that controlled your feelings?" said the Fourth Custodian half stating and half asking.

"Yes. Of course it was the circumstances. All normal people would react like I did, faced with what faced me," asserted the Apprentice.

"In what other ways could a human being have reacted to those same circumstances?" Realising that such a question, if it was to be answered by the Apprentice, would require a huge knowledge of both history and psychology, which at her age would be unlikely, the Fourth Custodian added: "During a prolonged conflict between eastern countries the generals of the stronger side noticed that when faced with execution those captured showed no fear, offered no resistance and even looked serene. Even when mock executions were conducted and the swords landed on the back of the necks of those who believed they were about to be decapitated they showed no fear. Why?"

"Perhaps they weren't normal?" replied the Apprentice while realising that this was probably her resistance to change speaking.

"From this historical period we know that almost all people from this society reacted as we've just described. They were as intelligent and civilised as you. Please accept my assurance that they were normal," elaborated the Fourth Custodian." Give me another explanation for their reaction."

Memories of her previous meetings came to the Apprentice's mind. She decided to risk thinking out loud knowing that this Fourth Custodian would help her in the same way that the others had.

"Perhaps they had such control over their behaviour that they could react or not react as they wished. Perhaps they had the kind of iron will that allows some people to overcome their natural urges," explored the Apprentice, as always revealing the power of her intelligence.

"Indeed. They do, sorry did, have total control over their behaviour. Did they allow circumstances to control their behaviour?"

"No, they did not, but maybe they had that iron will that I just suggested," retorted the Apprentice increasing her level of resistance. She could sense that a momentous and deeply threatening change was being asked of her and resistance seemed the only logical option.

"Let me assure you that their will power was also normal, yet they did not allow circumstances to control their behaviour, in even the most extreme of circumstances. Do circumstances control your behaviour, your feelings, your thoughts?"

"YES, my circumstances were just as extreme . . ." the Apprentice trailed off. "Well perhaps not quite as extreme," confessed the Apprentice.

"Tell me honestly, why did you just change your mind?" asked the Fourth Custodian.

"I don't know. I suppose I am resisting what you are asking me to consider. Why am I resisting this?" asked the Apprentice.

"Now that you are aware that you are resisting you will succeed. Your resistance comes from the same place that accounts for the behaviour of those eastern warriors. Try answering the question again as if you were not resisting. Will you do that for me?" asked the Fourth Custodian while wondering why almost everyone resists, why almost everyone places a whole range of barriers in their own way.

"I'll try not to resist, but I don't know if I can," replied the Apprentice honestly.

"Bring to mind each of the meetings that you have had with the other Custodians as you try to answer: Do circumstances control your behaviour, your feelings, your thoughts?"

The Apprentice fought in her mind. First she wanted to challenge the question itself. Then she questioned the point of all this discussion. She was promised The Perfect Gift and all she had received so far was challenge, torment and an unwelcome ride on an emotional roller-coaster. But she had promised to try not to resist.

The Fourth Custodian looked on compassionately as the Apprentice battled in her mind.

After some time she began: "Circumstances don't control my behaviour unless I let them . . . Neither do they control my feelings unless I let them . . . and my thoughts influence, maybe even control, how I feel and behave. That's what you want me to say, isn't it."

"I hope it is also the truth," replied the Fourth Custodian.

"If that is true why did I let myself react the way I did? I don't know, do you?"

"To answer that and to help you understand why you, and almost all intelligent people resist what we are discussing let me tell you of another society," the Fourth Custodian replied, avoiding the challenge and the confrontation that could easily arise by having reacted differently to the Apprentice's answer.

"In a far away land the people there celebrate the death of a loved one," the Fourth Custodian paused knowing what was coming next.

"They *what*?" the Apprentice's resistance level was increasing.

"They have a party and tell stories of the great good done by the person just deceased. They celebrate because they believe that a person only dies when they have been given permission by the Gods to walk among them," continued the Fourth Custodian. "Here in our culture we tend to mourn the death of a loved one, we tend to cry and feel bad." he paused again. "Why does the same event cause totally different reactions in the two societies?"

"Is it because in one society they *believe* one thing about death and in the other they believe something else," replied the Apprentice.

"Exactly. Beliefs explain the difference." The Fourth Custodian knew the Apprentice would be better at persuading herself than he could ever be, if only he could get her to figure out for herself the chain of internal events, so he asked: " What kinds of thoughts would they have about the death of a loved one based on the beliefs that they hold in that far away society?"

"Thoughts like, 'my relative has been blessed by the Gods, my relative is being celebrated by my community,' ' guessed the Apprentice.

"How would such thoughts make them feel?" continued the Fourth Custodian.

"Good, happy, or at very least not as sad as we would be."

Avoiding the temptation to pick at the edges of what she had said the Fourth Custodian continued: "Mostly, and how would feeling in the way you have described make them behave compared to us in our society when faced with the death of a loved one?"

"I suppose they would appear to be happy, they would behave in ways that demonstrated how they felt," guessed the Apprentice again.

"Explain to me the chain of events that seems to be happening here," said the Fourth Custodian.

"You are telling me that what people believe determines what they think, and that what they think determines how they feel, and how they feel and what they think determines how they behave, is that right?"

"Perhaps. Perhaps we should test what you have said

using your own experience," suggested the Fourth Custodian. "What would you have thought if you had believed that I was *acting* the part of a crazed gunman to make a point? What would you have felt? How would you have behaved?"

"I would have been thinking: 'why does he have to go to such extremes to make his point?' I would probably have felt a touch awkward trying to play along with your little game. I would have probably behaved in a rather stiff way," revealed the Apprentice honestly.

"Do you agree that your behaviour would have been different if you had believed something different about the circumstances?" asked the Fourth Custodian calmly.

"Yes," agreed the Apprentice.

"Can you tell me what controls how you think, feel and act? Circumstances or events, or, what you believe about those circumstances or events?"

"What I believe about circumstances or events," responded the Apprentice realising that her resistance was decreasing as her understanding was increasing.

"Yes. If you want to control what you think, what do you need to be able to control?" asked the Fourth Custodian with building enthusiasm.

"You want me to say 'what I believe' don't you? But how can anyone possibly control what they believe?"

"Yes, I do want you to say 'what I believe'? But do you think that is right?" asked a concerned Fourth Custodian seeing his goal slip away from him.

"Maybe sometimes." The Apprentice's resistance was still there.

"Which times?" asked the Fourth Custodian slowly.

"In each of the situations that you demonstrated to me."

"But, not in any others?" checked the Fourth Custodian.

"No, there may be others, but I don't know them."

"Take a guess at what other situations there may be where beliefs control your thoughts and your thoughts control your emotions and your thoughts and emotions together control your behaviour," encouraged the Fourth Custodian.

"All the situations similar to those you mentioned."

"Uh, huh." He encouraged her again.

"And maybe any situation that provokes strong emotions."

"Why do you clean your teeth?" asked the Fourth Custodian changing the mood with what seemed to the Apprentice an inappropriate question.

"What?" she replied somewhat startled.

"Why do you clean your teeth?" asked the Fourth Custodian again in exactly the same tone.

"To prevent my teeth from being damaged."

"Am I right in suggesting that you believe cleaning your teeth protects them from decay?"

"Yes, of course," she replied indignantly.

"Was there a time when people did not believe that

cleaning your teeth prevented decay?" asked the Fourth Custodian.

Feeling her resistance levels rising again the Apprentice answered: "I think we both know there was."

"And do you get emotional about cleaning your teeth?"

"Of course not." The Apprentice was getting irritated.

"Have we found an example of a situation in which your behaviour is based on a belief and you enact that behaviour with little or no emotion? And have we also found a situation in which a new belief changed the behaviour of millions or billions of people, believing that cleaning their teeth protects them?" The Fourth Custodian epitomised compassion.

The Apprentice did not want to agree, but she had no choice: "I suppose so."

"Would I be right in assuming that although your head is telling you: 'yes, beliefs do control thought, feeling and behaviour,' you don't want to accept it?"

"Yes. It seems somehow wrong."

"Why would people want to resist it?" asked the Fourth Custodian giving the Apprentice time and space to figure it out for herself.

"Because it means that I'm responsible for how I act, think, feel and behave. That's hard to accept." the Apprentice surprised herself.

"Why should accepting that responsibility be so hard?" The Fourth Custodian knew that the Apprentice was close.

"It means all the pain I have felt was my fault. All the times my behaviour has led to consequences I didn't want were my fault, all the . . ." There was a very long pause before the Apprentice continued: "It would mean that anytime I felt bad in the future, any time I did something stupid in the future, any time I had bad thoughts in the future . . . It would all be my fault."

"Is that true?" asked the Fourth Custodian.

"It may be true, but it's too much to bear!" the Apprentice stated decisively.

"Have you ever thought of going into politics, that was great rhetoric?" the Fourth Custodian enthused.

They both smiled.

He went on: "What price would people pay if what we say is true and they continue living as if others or other things were responsible for their beliefs, their thoughts, their emotions and their behaviours? What would they miss out on? What opportunities would pass them by? What personal growth would they miss?" the Fourth Custodian paused, realising that he too was using rhetoric. "Even though it is tough to accept, what are the benefits of accepting that you are totally responsible for how you think, act and feel?"

"I can't imagine!"

"How would you like the ability to feel anyway you wanted, right now? How would you like to feel fantastic this moment?"

"I'd love to."

"How would you like to be able to control your

47

thoughts, feelings and behaviours so that you could achieve whatever you wanted – within human limits of course?" asked the Fourth Custodian trying not to get carried away.

"That would turn me into some kind of robot!"

"Does a robot have control over its programming? No. Would you like to be able to do those things that you told the First Custodian you could not, even though you told yourself you wanted to. Would you like to be able to stop doing the things that you've told yourself you want to, but can't? Would being able to do those things make you a robot?" The Fourth Custodian sensed that he was closer this time.

"No, I mean yes . . . I mean, no, it would not make me a robot to be able to control myself in that way, not if I am still the programmer," the Apprentice said confirming the Fourth Custodian's proposition.

"In the chain of internal events we described, where does control begin?" asked the Fourth Custodian with an air of finality.

"It begins with what I believe, but I don't know how to control what I believe," replied the Apprentice protesting that she could not finish, not yet. "Can you show me how to control what I believe?"

"That will be the job of the Fifth Custodian, tomorrow. Thankyou for giving me the honour of helping you."

"I don't want to seem ungrateful, but I was promised The Perfect Gift, and all I have had so far is a series of interesting discussions with some very interesting people. Is that The Perfect Gift, a series of discussions?" protested the Apprentice trying very hard not to sound grasping.

"The Perfect Gift is a lot more than a few conversations, and if you can be patient for a few more meetings you will receive The Perfect Gift and it will be worth much more than all the other gifts you could have chosen. Can you be patient for a little longer?"

"Yes, I hope so . . . and thank*you* for being so patient with me. I am aware that I can be awkward and clumsy with people who are trying to help me," the Apprentice said with genuine gratitude.

"It is truly my honour. One more thing, could you write a summary of everything you have discussed so far in your meetings?"

The Apprentice sat down to write her summary. Taking out her previous summary as a guide she asked herself: "Why did I argue so much about beliefs being the starting point in the internal chain of events that control behaviour? Is it really such a huge addition to what I have already agreed? Why so much thanks from the people who are helping me?" she thought to herself while adding to her current list.

I am in control of my behaviour.

I am in control of my feelings.

What I feel controls how I behave.

How I behave feeds back to influence how I feel.

What I think influences what I feel and therefore how I behave.

I am in control of what I think.

What I think is influenced or controlled by what I believe.

What I believe is the start of the internal chain that determines how I behave.

But how do I control what I believe?

Chapter 7

The Fifth Custodian

A huge sign on the door of the building said: 'Welcome to the Apprentice of Life, please come in.' The Apprentice walked in to a very elegant reception area. Sitting at the desk was a strikingly handsome young man. Many movie stars would pay large amounts of money to acquire such a captivating face.

"You must be here to see my mother," he said causing the Apprentice some concern that she had been recognised in a place where she knew no one.

"I don't know, I was just told to come here at this time," she replied.

"In that case I am absolutely sure that it is you. Please come with me, she is expecting you." The Apprentice followed.

"Mum, this is your visitor," said the young man as he led the Apprentice into a room and closed the door behind her.

"Please, Apprentice of Life, come in, have a seat, and please, accept my thanks that you have given me the opportunity to help you," said the Fifth Custodian.

Expecting a similar pattern to before the Apprentice asked: "What surprises do *you* have in mind for me?"

"You are apprehensive, and I imagine, you believe something that will provoke a strong reaction in you will happen here today," observed the Fifth Custodian.

"Of course, I have absolutely no good reason to believe that," replied the Apprentice with a rich mixture of apprehension and irony in her voice.

"We'll come back to what you have just said, but to answer your question, I am going to tell you a couple of simple stories, and then ask you some questions. Are you happy with that?" asked the Fifth Custodian with that same 'you are safe with me; all I do for you will bring you good' tone the Apprentice had heard from all the Custodians.

The Apprentice thought: "I must ask them about that tone. I must ask about these strange titles and mysterious meetings."

"Ehm, yes. It will make a nice change to be entertained rather than terrified," she said in reply to the question she had nearly forgotten was asked.

"Let me tell you about a child who was born with a serious leg and ankle disability before such things were as easy to correct as they are today. As a partially, but not seriously disabled child she was badly enough disabled to be excluded by other able bodied children, but not disabled enough to be sent to a school for such children. She grew up being bullied and verbally abused when she tried to join in and feeling as though she could not contribute the rest of the time. Her grades were poor; she seemed to pay little attention in class.

"Her mother was truly wise. She knew that her daughter longed for her mobility, to be able to move around like other kids. She also knew that her daughter was feeling excluded and believed that she could not contribute.

"How do you get a child who believes they can't contribute to offer something that would enable them to join in with other kids? How do you overcome years of subtle but effective conditioning? You can't just say: 'Go to them and join in.' How do you get a child in such circumstances to change her beliefs?

"Months passed as the child's mother struggled with the problem. She ensured that the child joined in everything that took place at home. Even in the major decisions. But at school her daughter was still isolated, unpopular with some and ignored by most.

"Then one day the child brought a note back from school. It said that all the children would sit an exam in six months time that was sat by all 11 year olds.

"At last, the solution: 'If you come top in your school exam you will receive the bike of your choice,' said the mother to her daughter. 'What bike would you like?'

"The child knew a bike was her route to joining in. She chose one. She would get that bike whatever it took. She was mostly unaware of the financial sacrifice that her family was making.

"The child started paying attention in class. She did

all the homework. She stayed in the classroom at break-times and lunchtimes. Anything and everything she did not understand she asked the teachers, went back to her desk, checked that she did understand and asked again if she did not. She asked questions constantly. Nothing, but nothing was going to stop her becoming mobile.

"Exam day came.

"Results day came.

"The headmaster read out the results in descending order. The child waited. As progressively lower scores were being read out her score was still not there. As the name of a person she knew did no work, and put in no effort, was read out, scoring as expected, her heartbreak was complete. She had come last. No bike, no mobility, and now failure as well.

"The headmaster continued: 'And now for the last score . . .' He was going to read out her name and score; her failure and humiliation would be total ' . . . has scored higher in the exam than anyone in this school for 20 years.'

"The tears of despair that had been running down her face turned to tears of joy.

"'She must have cheated!' shouted one of the brightest kids who had been unexpectedly beaten by a *huge* margin.

"'Yeah, she must have copied,' protested another child.

"The tears of joy turned again to sobs of disappointment and disbelief. She said nothing. She could say nothing.

"The Headmaster took control seeing the sadness in his new star pupil's face: 'If she cheated, if she copied, from whom did she copy? She answered every single question correctly. Nobody else did that. How could she have copied? *Whom* could she have copied? Well?'

"A child spoke up. 'I know she didn't cheat because she helped me with Maths.'

" 'She helped me with English.' concurred another.

" 'She helped me with History.'

" 'And me.'

"In all twelve voices spoke up and defended the child.

"Twelve friends had suddenly appeared. And yes, she had helped them. In fact she had helped more, but the others did not speak up.

"In her attempts to get the bike she wanted so much she had been learning fast. Some of the other kids noticed that she had answered questions that they were struggling with. They asked her how? She helped them without even thinking about it.

"That day her mother collected her from school, took her to a warehouse owned by a close friend of the family. There was a gathering of adults, her family – all of her family. They were standing around something draped in canvass. Of course, it was the bike the child had dreamt of for so long.

"In front of the people she loved she received the reward that would now give her mobility. But, long before it gave her mobility the dream of that bike had given her something much more valuable; it had enabled her to contribute.

"That little girl is now a Number 1 best-selling author, professor and consultant to many of the most senior CEOs in our country. She contributes massively to her society," finished the Fifth Custodian.

Holding back her tears of joy, the Apprentice of Life asked: "Is that a true story?"

"Yes, it is."

"Who was, I mean, is the little girl?" asked the Apprentice.

"I was that little girl," replied the Fifth Custodian with total humility.

"But, you don't look disabled." whispered the Apprentice still recovering from her emotional reaction.

"Without my special shoes and various other supports, I'm sorry to say that I do. But we're not here to talk about me. Tell me, what did the mother do for her child. Sorry, what did my mother do for me?"

"She gave you a reason to work hard."

"Yes, that's true. Let me remind you of an implied question I asked you earlier. I said to you 'you're apprehensive, and probably suspect that I'm going to provoke you into something.' You replied: 'I have good reason to believe so.' Is that right?"

"Pretty much," agreed the Apprentice.

"Do you need good reasons to believe something, or

can you just believe any old nonsense that you want?" the Fifth Custodian asked in a somewhat leading way.

"Yes of course. You need reasons to believe *anything*. You can't just believe anything without good reason," asserted the Apprentice.

"Can you change your beliefs for no good reason?" continued the Fifth Custodian's line of reasoning.

"No, when I've changed my beliefs in the past it has always been for good reasons."

"What did my mother do that gave me reason to change my misplaced childhood belief that I could not contribute?" continued the Fifth Custodian.

"By offering you the bike in exchange for top notch school performance she gave you the motivation to acquire something that you then used to contribute," replied the Apprentice in a way that made the fifth Custodian sure that she too would one day make a great Custodian.

"Yes, that's it. What did being able to contribute do to my original belief?" said the Fifth Custodian sensing she could move up to the next step soon.

"It overturned your belief. Being able to contribute made believing that you couldn't a crazy belief to hold," replied the Apprentice.

"Great. How do you change your beliefs?" asked the Fifth Custodian.

"You wait for evidence to contradict what you currently believe," said the Apprentice of Life.

"So close yet so far," thought the Fifth Custodian.

"What can you do to change your beliefs if evidence has not happened to arrive on the day you want to make a change?" asked the Fifth Custodian.

"According to you Custodians, I wouldn't want to change my beliefs because any *want* would have come from my beliefs. Why would my beliefs want to change themselves?" asked the Apprentice, thinking that she had just killed the Custodian's argument.

"Do you remember when the Chair of the Custodians said that intelligence more often than not gets in the way of acquiring The Perfect Gift?" the Fifth Custodian enquired.

"Yes . . . Am I doing that?" asked the Apprentice.

"You are, but it is my responsibility to find another way to help you. Give me a minute." With that the Fifth Custodian put her palms together briefly and began.

"Will you be totally honest with me, knowing that as a Custodian I will only ever help you?" asked the Fifth Custodian.

"If it helps you."

"Tell me about one of your most vivid memories," requested the Custodian.

After the Apprentice had finished recounting the details of the memory the Fifth Custodian asked: "On a scale of 0 to 10 how real does that incident feel to you now after all these years?"

"It is all a bit hazy; maybe a four or a five."

"I'm going to tell you a story about you and your past. Imagine that it is actually happening as I go through it.

Close your eyes and follow me," instructed the Fifth Custodian.

"When you were 11 you had a life changing experience. Imagine you are where I describe. You are at a public meeting with your family. You are in a big hall. It is wonderfully decorated with gold carvings and crystal chandeliers, and a stage curtain, which alone, looks as though it is worth more than most houses. Tell me more about this wonderful hall."

Two minutes later the Apprentice had completed a wonderful picture.

"Which of your family is standing on your left? What are they wearing? Who is on your right, what are they wearing?" continued the Fifth Custodian.

The Apprentice obliged.

"Tell me what you can smell. What can you feel both emotionally and physically? What temperature is it? What are you wearing?"

The Apprentice obliged again.

"The chair of the meeting stands up and makes an announcement. One of the greatest leaders the world has ever seen is here on an unexpected visit and has asked if they can address the audience. Would the audience like that to happen? They would. The leader comes onto the stage. Describe the person who came onto the stage? What were they wearing? What did they sound like? What did they look like? What was their voice like?"

The Apprentice obliged yet again.

"The leader asks a question directed at the children in the audience: 'What do you think of war?' After asking a few others the leader asks you the same question. Your face becomes red with self-awareness. Tell me how it feels in detail."

The Apprentice continued to oblige.

"You answer by saying that you don't know enough about why people fight to be able to say; maybe you'll know when you are older.

"At the end of the meeting there are refreshments and biscuits. The leader comes up to your family and asks permission to address you. As the leader is speaking a feeling of overwhelming peace comes over you. Tell me what that feels like?" asked the Fifth Custodian.

After the Apprentice finished the Custodian continued: "The leader asks you how old you are and what you want to do when you are older. You say you don't know. The leader then asks what you find most interesting. You tell the leader. The leader asks more questions. You tell the leader more. Your enthusiasm for the subject takes over and your speech flows. What did you say you were interested in, and how did it feel to be enthusing so much?"

The Apprentice finished her description.

"The great leader listens intensely until you have said everything you want to. Your family members are looking on with their eyes and jaws wide open. The leader says to you: 'Young lady, I have had the privilege of meeting thousands of the world's most talented people, and I have something to tell you, you have something in common with them. I believe that you can achieve anything that you want to.' In that moment the world stops. Here is this great person telling *you* that *you* can achieve anything that you want to, and because you can feel the leader's wisdom you just know it is true. Tell me how that feels. What was the leader's facial expression as they spoke?"

The Apprentice described in detail what she felt and what she saw.

"Can you say to yourself that you can feel that you are there with that leader right now? How real are the words of the leader to you?" asked the Fifth Custodian.

"Totally on both counts," replied the Apprentice.

"How real does your mind think the event is?"

"Completely," replied the Apprentice. "Ten on your scale of 10."

"Do you feel that the meeting with the great leader could influence your thinking now; that it could make you feel that you had somehow been assured of your destiny by someone who knows?" asked the Fifth Custodian.

"Yeah, pretty much," replied the Apprentice.

"Do you remember that I asked you: 'What can you do to change your beliefs if evidence has not happened to arrive to justify making the change?" asked the Fifth Custodian.

"Yes."

"Try answering that question now," encouraged the Custodian.

The Apprentice started hesitantly: "If I want to believe something I need to find evidence or create evidence to justify it to myself, is that right?"

"Oh, yes, completely and absolutely right. Well done. And would you say that you can also choose what you believe?" asked the Fifth Custodian.

"No."

"No?" began the Fifth Custodian "You think you can change . . ."

The Apprentice of Life interrupted: "You can't choose what you believe. The society that you live in controls what you, what I believe. If I had been brought up in a different society I would hold different beliefs." At last the Apprentice had found what she was sure was the flaw with the Fifth Custodian's line of reasoning.

"Hmmm", the Fifth Custodian thought to herself, "it is some time since I heard that. How do I . . . oh, yes," she thought and then asked the Apprentice: "How does society control your beliefs?"

"I have to hold certain beliefs to fit into society." The Apprentice knew she had the killer argument.

"What would happen if you did not hold those beliefs?" replied the Fifth Custodian in that same calm reassuring voice the Apprentice had heard so many times now.

"I would miss out on all opportunities economic, social, educational and leisure," asserted the Apprentice.

The Fifth Custodian simply and calmly replied: "How?"

"If I don't hold these beliefs I wouldn't be given access to the benefits that I want."

"You choose to hold your beliefs to get access to the benefits you want?" asked the Fifth Custodian with a tone that suggested, 'even if you are wrong nothing but good will come from this'.

"Yes, don't you?" The Apprentice was not so sure now. In fact she didn't know whether she did consciously choose her beliefs or not.

"So, you choose what you believe?"

"No, not really. If I didn't hold those beliefs I wouldn't get the benefits I want, so there is no choice," resumed the Apprentice regaining her flow.

"And there are no other ways to secure the benefits that you want?" asked the Fifth Custodian, again sending the signal that being wrong will be OK.

"No."

"There is absolutely no other way to secure the benefits that you want than to adopt en masse the beliefs of the society in which you live?" quizzed the Fifth Custodian in a way that from anyone else would have sounded provocative.

"Ehm . . ." The Apprentice paused for thought as she realised her position was untenable, "Well, possibly there are a few other ways."

"Choose an area of life and name a few."

There was a long pause until the Apprentice replied:

"I suppose that I could form sporting societies with other people who did or wanted to hold the same beliefs that I did."

"Yes, most new groupings of all kinds are formed by people thinking just like that," confirmed and elaborated the Fifth Custodian. "Name some other ways in which you could secure the economic benefits you want."

Immediately the Apprentice replied: "There aren't any. If I don't fit into existing companies by believing what they believe I'm out."

"What do people who can't stomach selling their soul to companies or organisations whose beliefs clash with theirs do to earn a living?" The Fifth Custodian sensed that this time the Apprentice's intelligence would be an asset.

"Uh . . . they set up their own businesses or work for themselves or find an organisation which believes what they believe," replied the Apprentice with a look of insight in her eyes.

"Yes, and what happens to people who choose to comply with, and who try to live by, beliefs that are alien to them, in order to get access to benefits? What do such people look like?" asked the Fifth Custodian trying to show the Apprentice the other side of the coin.

"Oh yes. They look empty some of them. Others look angry or resentful. Most are lacking drive and initiative. Many just look miserable," replied the Apprentice surprised at the observation she had made but until that point had not articulated.

"How many of these people are there?" asked the Fifth Custodian trying to give the Apprentice an awareness of the scale of the observation she had just made.

"Most?" quizzed the Apprentice with considerable uncertainty.

"Possibly. It does seem to be a large number. Perhaps we should leave it to the social scientists to discover just how many people lead such lives." The Fifth Custodian paused. "How do people who take control of their beliefs appear compared to those you have just described?"

Replying with a laugh in her voice the Apprentice said: "I don't know any."

"Are you sure?" asked the Fifth Custodian alerting the Apprentice to the fact that there were some she knew but had overlooked.

"Of course, sorry. I know five people who seem to control their beliefs."

"Who are they?" asked the Fifth Custodian knowing that the Apprentice had already identified who by numbering them.

"Each of the Custodians I have met." The Apprentice felt obliged to say it.

"How do people who control their beliefs appear?" re-asked the Fifth Custodian.

"You all seem happy, radiant ... eh ... cheerful, compassionate . . . grateful, supportive, healthy."

"Do you want to be like those who do not control their beliefs or like those who do?" asked the Fifth Custodian.

"Obviously like those who control their beliefs."

"OK. Do you agree that you can choose as well as change your beliefs?" asked the Fifth Custodian.

"Yes."

"Right you are. So let's pull together what we have covered so far," began the Fifth Custodian. "Can you change what you believe? Can you choose what to believe?"

"Yes. I mean I can change my beliefs and I can choose them. And the other thing we covered was that to change or choose my beliefs I must find or create the evidence to justify doing so."

"You now have every reason to celebrate!" exclaimed the Fifth Custodian. "For you are one step away from The Perfect Gift," she glowed.

"Hold on. All I have done is answer a few questions and you are telling me I am one step away from The Perfect Gift, what do you mean? What is this Perfect Gift?" demanded the Apprentice.

"All your questions will be answered tomorrow by the Sixth Custodian. Can you be patient for one more day?" asked the Fifth Custodian concerned that the Apprentice was so close to her Perfect Gift yet still seeming not to grasp the enormity of it.

"Yes, I can hold out for one more day. I suppose you're going to tell me to write a summary of what we have discussed here today."

"Yes, I am. I am also going to ask you to accept my thanks for giving me the chance to help you here today. It has been a real privilege. Thankyou."

After thanking the Fifth Custodian, apologising for her impatience and disguising her irritation at this continual thanksgiving the Apprentice left and on the way home wrote her summary:

I am in control of my behaviour.

I am in control of my feelings.

What I feel controls how I behave.

How I behave feeds back to influence how I feel.

What I think influences what I feel and therefore how I behave.

I am in control of what I think.

What I think is influenced or controlled by what I believe.

What I believe is the start of the internal chain that determines how I behave.

I can change what I believe.

I can choose what I believe.

If I can choose what I believe, I can control what I think and then what I feel and therefore how I behave.

But how do I really choose or change what I believe?

What does all this mean?

Chapter 8

The Sixth Custodian

"How am I supposed to find someone at a property auction?" thought the Apprentice as she arrived. "There must be 300 people here. Damn, there are no seats left. I'll stand at the back where I can see what is going on."

When the first 20 lots had been sold the Auctioneer announced a break. Just as the Apprentice was getting a drink in the adjoining room a slightly slurred voice said: "Are you looking for the Sixth Custodian?"

"Yes, I a . . ." said the Apprentice as she turned, having her words choked by the shock of what she saw. It was a man, maybe. His face was deeply scarred, not from cuts, but from very, very serious burns. His ears had been burned off, as had his nose and hair. The skin around his eyes was very damaged creating an appearance of a major eye deformity. The reason his speech was slurred was that much of his lips had also succumbed to whatever horrible thing had happened to him.

"It is me you are looking for, I am the Sixth Custodian. It is a pleasure to meet you," he said as he extended his hand, a hand that had stumps where full-length fingers had once been. Glancing quickly at his other hand the Apprentice noticed it was similarly damaged.

She gingerly extended her hand cautious of doing damage by offering a normal squeeze. Just as she said: "It is a pleasure to meet you too," she discovered that there was no need to worry; this was a man who had a grip stronger than most men.

"Your eyes tell me that you need to ask about my accident. I have bought what I need, so if you wish we can go for a meal and you can ask all you need to. I know it is early, but by the time we get there and get settled it will be lunch time." The Sixth Custodian had such a cheerful and happy voice.

"Yes, I would love to have lunch and to ask you many questions. I am sorry if I reacted to you in such a way that offended you," the Apprentice said with deep sincerity.

"I'm sure no offence was intended and you should be sure that none was taken. Shall we go?" said the Sixth Custodian gesturing to the door.

The hotel where they stopped was enormous. The restaurant on its own was bigger than most hotels. The Apprentice said half out loud and half talking to herself: "It is a pleasure to just walk in through the door. I can't wait to discover what the food must be like." She had never been near, let alone in, such a prestigious environment.

"Your usual table?" said the headwaiter with a distinct tone of humour in a voice that sounded like Royalty.

"Yes, thankyou. How are you today?" the Sixth Custodian enquired.

"All the better for seeing the boss back from his jolly." The headwaiter was almost laughing.

"He owns this place, and what's more he has a great relationship with his staff," thought the Apprentice as they were shown to a table overlooking an elegant lake, which was full of wildlife.

"Do you own this place?" asked the Apprentice.

"Yes, I do, but I think you have other more important questions than that to ask me. You can ask me anything you like about the Custodians, The Perfect Gift, anything that has happened or been discussed in your meetings," the Sixth Custodian said with nearly a laugh in his voice too.

The Apprentice thought: "Does he always have such a cheerful tone?" Then entering the world of speech: "There is so much to ask you that I don't know where to start."

"Perhaps I can overcome what might be a barrier to our communication. Do you want to know what happened to me?" asked the Sixth Custodian again with total joy in his voice.

"I'd rather not if it makes you uncomfortable," replied the Apprentice, being acutely aware of the sensitivity of the moment.

"This happened 20 years ago. I have had just a little

time to get used to it. But it is new and awkward for you, is that right?" asked the Sixth Custodian.

The Apprentice suddenly felt exceptionally self-conscious: "Uhm, yes . . . I have to admit it, yes, it is difficult for me to ask you about it."

"What must you believe to make you feel awkward and self-conscious?" asked the Sixth Custodian, still almost laughing.

"What do you mean?" replied the Apprentice not quite understanding what was being asked of her.

"You feel awkward and self-conscious. You have learned from the other Custodians that you are responsible for how you feel. What you are thinking about my appearance is making you feel awkward. And those thoughts are coming directly from your beliefs. Is the internal chain I have just described accurate?"

"I suppose it must be, but I don't want to offend you. Surely I can't believe such . . ." The Apprentice was cut-off by the Sixth Custodian holding up what was left of his right hand.

"Please, do not be hard on yourself. Your reaction and your beliefs are very, very common. Hundreds of millions of people are just as you are. We should use your reaction as a learning opportunity. Will you help me do that? And will you promise not to blame yourself as we do?"

"Yes," replied the Apprentice while thinking: "This man is amazing. Here he is using his extreme disfigurement to help me, and what is more he seems to be enjoying it."

"Right. Tell me what you were thinking immediately as I asked you if you wanted to know what happened to me," asked the Sixth Custodian.

The Apprentice hesitated and could not think of anything to say.

"OK, tell me what you are thinking now," said the Sixth Custodian rescuing the Apprentice.

"You really want to know?"

The Sixth Custodian still sounding as though he were just about to break out into a laugh replied: "Yes, and please tell me everything. To reassure you, you should know I have been a Custodian for many years and that I have had this discussion with many, many people. Nothing you can say will shock or offend me."

"I was thinking, 'how do I ask without offending? If I say the wrong thing I will destroy our relationship before it has begun. Should I even be wanting to ask? Do I have the right to ask?"

"Well done, it takes most people about 10 minutes to get to the point you have reached already. Now, tell me, how would such thoughts make you feel," said the wonderfully happy voice.

"As I did feel. Awkward. Anxious. Confused," said the Apprentice beginning to relax.

"Absolutely, and from where did such thoughts come? What must you believe in order to think the thoughts you did?"

"Ehm . . ."

"Write down the thoughts you had," suggested the Sixth Custodian.

After writing them on a page in her diary the Apprentice asked: "What did you want me to do with this? Oh, yes, you wanted me to say what I must believe to have thoughts like this."

"Yes, take: 'How do I ask without offending?' What would you have to believe to think that?" asked the Sixth Custodian.

"Ehmm . . . That I must not offend this person."

"Yes, what else?" asked the Sixth Custodian.

"Uhm . . . That asking about the injuries would cause pain for you."

"Good so far. Go on."

"That I have no right to pry into something as painful and traumatic as that must have been – I mean to lose your . . ." The Apprentice's voice dropped off.

"What does the fact that your voice just trailed off tell you about your beliefs?" asked the Sixth Custodian still on the verge of laughter.

"That I do believe that your loss must have been painful and that I also believe that even saying what you lost will bring back the pain for you. And that I should not do that," tentatively offered the Apprentice.

"Great! How would such beliefs make you or anyone think? How would such beliefs ultimately make you or anyone feel in the same circumstances you just experienced?" asked the Sixth Custodian.

"Awkward, anxious, confused thoughts. They would make you feel and behave awkwardly too in the presence of anyone who had experienced a physical loss."

"Oh, it is a real pleasure to help you! Outcomes; what would be the result of such behaviour?" glowed the Sixth Custodian.

"Eh . . . An unsuccessful relationship. You wouldn't be able to get on feeling and behaving like that." The Apprentice was now more relaxed and flowing.

"Yes. Show me the connection between how you behave and what result you obtain?" requested the Sixth Custodian.

"There is nothing to show. How you behave directly affects the result you achieve . . . In almost all circumstances." The Apprentice was close to acquiring The Perfect Gift, but nothing was further from her mind.

"So right. Sometimes no matter how you behave, the outcome will be the same. But that is very, very rare." The Sixth Custodian could sense that the Apprentice was in the zone. She was totally engaged and unaware of anything other than answering the questions asked of her. "Pull it all together now. Tell me what the connection is between events, beliefs, thoughts, emotions, behaviours and results. Write it down or draw it before you tell me, if that helps."

After a few enthusiastic and progressively clearer attempts to document the connections, the Apprentice looked deep into the eyes of the Sixth Custodian: "I think I have it. The results we obtain in life are mostly controlled by us, and specifically by how we behave, by what we do. How we behave is largely controlled by how we feel and what we think. What we think is not caused by the events or circumstances we create or experience, but by how we interpret those events and circumstances; what we believe controls what we think.''

''Wow! You got there first time. I have never had that before in all my years as a Custodian.''

They smiled at each other and basked in their joint achievement.

''Tell me what happened to you?'' asked the Apprentice feeling that she could. She knew, somehow, that the Sixth Custodian could not only handle the discussion but would probably use it as another learning opportunity.

''Before I went into property and property-based businesses I used to buy, renovate and sell cars. I had a small garage. One day, when I was re-spraying a classic car that I had bought at an auction for a very low price, the two ventilation fans I had to take the flammable fumes out of the garage both failed. Today such an event would sound an alarm, but back then . . . It was only a matter of time before I generated a spark in a garage environment. What you see is what happened in the fireball that followed. Sadly, the car didn't make it.''

The Sixth Custodian smiled, but the Apprentice did not.

''It sounds as though *you* were lucky to survive,'' said the Apprentice in a hushed tone.

"Yes, I was, and if I had not already possessed The Perfect Gift I am sure the loss would have killed me faster than the actual injuries."

"What do you mean?" asked the Apprentice.

"If I had not had what The Perfect Gift gave me I would have given up and died."

"I still don't understand. What do you mean? What did The Perfect Gift give you? What is The Perfect Gift?" asked the Apprentice.

"I'd like to answer that question later," replied the Sixth Custodian. "For now I'd like to explore the connection between all the elements you correctly described. Tell me, if you want to achieve a particular result what must happen before that?"

"You have to behave in a way that achieves the result." The Apprentice still wanted an answer to her question, but she was prepared to indulge the Sixth Custodian.

"Yes, the way you behave, what you do, determines the result you achieve."

"And if you want to change the result you get what do you have to do?" asked the Sixth Custodian.

"Change your behaviour," immediately replied the Apprentice.

"To change your behaviour, what have you got to change?" enthused the Sixth Custodian.

"The way you feel." The Apprentice was getting the hang of this question and answer session.

"You know my next question, don't you?" teased the Sixth Custodian.

"Yes. 'To change what I feel, what do I need to change?' I need to change what I think. And if I may, your next question will be: 'To change what I think what do I need to change?' Is that right?"

"Getting good at this you are. And your answer?" rejoined the Sixth Custodian realising that the Apprentice was teasing him.

"I would have to change what I believe."

"And how do you change what you believe?" continued the Sixth Custodian.

"By finding or creating the justification to believe whatever I choose to." The Apprentice was sounding more like a Custodian than an Apprentice.

"And how do you decide what to believe?" asked the Sixth Custodian, pushing to see just how far the Apprentice could take her thinking unaided.

"Uhm . . . Eh . . ." She was struggling.

"You decide what you believe by . . ." started the Sixth Custodian.

"NO! Don't. Please," interrupted the Apprentice gradually turning her initially barked order into a request. "Let me figure it out for myself. Uhm . . . You decide what you need to believe by working backwards through the chain. By asking what result you want. By asking what behaviours that will require. By asking what feelings and thoughts those behaviours will require and what beliefs will be needed to generate those thoughts, feeling and behaviours."

"Fantastic," celebrated the Sixth Custodian, "Now figure out how you would take a belief that you wanted to adopt because of what it would give you and turn it into something permanent," directed the Sixth Custodian after sensing that the Apprentice was best at figuring things out for herself.

"You mean how do I make a belief part of me?" clarified the Apprentice.

"Yes."

"Ahhh . . . By using it. Yes, by consciously filtering what I experience and think through that belief. Is that right?" guessed the Apprentice.

"Yes, mostly. You can do that, but it is harder to make it work by forcing yourself to believe something. If you wanted to persuade someone that the world was spherical and not flat how would you do it?" asked the Sixth Custodian beginning another game.

"By showing them evidence, perhaps," played the Apprentice.

"And if they were still not persuaded what would you do?"

"Show them even more evidence?" offered the Apprentice.

"And if they were still not persuaded?" asked the Sixth Custodian.

"Either write them off as being mentally challenged or devise someway of getting them to experience for themselves that the earth was spherical." The Apprentice was enjoying the game.

"Got it! So how do you persuade yourself to change a belief you hold, or adopt a new belief you want to hold?" The Sixth Custodian was on the verge of letting laughter take over from speech.

"Could it, by any chance, have something to do with finding the evidence to persuade myself and giving myself the experiences to justify holding the new or changed belief?"

"A+," was all the Sixth Custodian needed to say.

They both laughed at the conclusion to their little game.

The Sixth Custodian changed his tone; he was deadly serious: "If you wanted to feel any way you wanted, what would you have to do?"

"Oh, that's easy," began the Apprentice confidently. "Ah . . . Oh dear. That's not so easy . . ." Her pitch dropped. ". . . I could choose to think thoughts that made me feel good."

The Sixth Custodian gestured for her to continue.

"Or I could address the beliefs that were preventing me from thinking feel-good thoughts."

"Yes. With this knowledge that you have just figured out for yourself what can you do?" asked the Sixth Custodian.

The Apprentice thought while looking into space and then proclaimed: "I can make myself feel anyway I want to, anytime I want to, regardless of what is happening around me, regardless of what is happening to me, can't I?"

"Yes. And?"

"I can choose how to think, what to think, how to behave, what to believe, what I want to achieve," continued the Apprentice. Then her eyes lit up; her expression turned into a full glow. "I now have The Perfect Gift, don't I?"

"You have."

"It is so simple, but it changes everything! How can anything so simple have such huge effects on our lives?" asked the Apprentice not really expecting an answer and then after having stopped as if frozen in time said: "I've always had The Perfect Gift, haven't I?"

"You have."

"I can, we all can, make ourselves feel anyway we want, anytime we want. We can think what we want anytime we want. We can behave anyway we want, anytime we want. We can even control what we achieve by controlling everything that comes first in the chain of mental events. Can't we?"

"We can."

"It truly is The Perfect Gift, isn't it? Any other gift may lead you to feel happy for a short while, but then it passes. By contrast, The Perfect Gift can give you that feeling, as often or for as long as you want. Can't it?" The ex-Apprentice was filling with more and more enthusiasm as she saw more and more clearly the value and power of The Perfect Gift.

"Wonderful! Only one little correction required: No gift leads you to or *makes* you feel happy. Only what you believe and what you think can lead to any emotion. *You* are in charge of how you feel, not any event, not any gift." The Sixth Custodian was full of joy. Another young life had been changed for the better, forever.

"Yes, of course. But, why doesn't everyone know this?" asked the ex-Apprentice getting caught up in her enthusiasm; already sensing that The Perfect Gift should be made available to everyone.

"I will answer that question, but first we have some unfinished business. You had some questions about the Custodians?" asked the Sixth Custodian not really expecting the Apprentice to want any answers to her previous questions, not now that she could see the full value and power of The Perfect Gift.

"I think I know why you call yourselves the Custodians." The Apprentice paused looking for approval to continue.

She got it from a nod.

"You are the keepers, the Custodians of The Perfect Gift." The Apprentice once again surprised the Sixth Custodian. "Your role is to keep intact the knowledge of The Perfect Gift so that you can give it away. The duty of the Custodians is to give away the knowledge of The Perfect Gift. That is what you have done for me."

"Right on all counts. You will make a great Custodian when your time comes," the Sixth Custodian said with great sincerity.

"How did you become a Custodian?" asked the graduating Apprentice.

"After the accident, when I was in hospital, and dying, according to the doctors. I remembered my journey to acquire The Perfect Gift. Until that point I had understood it, but never fully put it into practice. My circumstances were extreme; I knew the best chance I had of surviving was to harness The Perfect Gift fully. It worked. It saved my life, or rather, it allowed me to save my own life.

"Then, when I was out of danger, I had the same kinds of discussions with some of the other patients that you have had with the Custodians you have met. Many of them did for themselves what I had done. Word got back to the Custodians I had seen when I was your age, and they reminded me of my oath to pass on the help I had received and asked me if I would join them. Needless to say, having had my life saved by The Perfect Gift I was delighted to pass it on," concluded the Sixth Custodian.

"Each of the Custodians seemed more grateful to meet me than I was to meet them. Why was that? No. Hold on. Was it because they knew the value and power of what they were doing for me and I did not? Was it because they knew that this would change my life for the better, and they were the ones able to make that happen?"

"It is simply a great honour to be able to give someone the most valuable gift ever, The Perfect Gift. I must thank you for giving me that honour. Thankyou," said the Sixth Custodian with great humility.

"How do I become a Custodian? How do I have the honour of passing this on?"

"You can give The Perfect Gift to anyone and everyone you like, but please do not describe what you say to others as The Perfect Gift. People will not understand you. People will resist your attempts to help them. They will not believe that the happiness and anything else that they want can be achieved so easily," cautioned the Sixth Custodian.

"But I believe it, I have accepted it, others will too," protested the ex-Apprentice.

"Yes, you do. Yes, you have. Cast your mind back to how many days it took to reach this point. Think of the elaborate programme that a group of very dedicated people designed specifically for you, to help you get to this point. Remember, too, how much you resisted our attempts to help you. Remember all the arguments and objections you raised."

"Yes, I remember," conceded the ex-Apprentice with considerable embarrassment. "Is each giving of The Perfect Gift tailor made?"

"It has to be. Although the Custodians have to protect the knowledge of The Perfect Gift in order to give it away, it must be given so that there is the maximum likelihood it will be used, and perpetuated. In other words, we want as many people as possible who choose

The Perfect Gift to become Custodians after they have mastered The Perfect Gift fully."

The Sixth Custodian paused and took on a much more serious air. He looked into the eyes of the ex-Apprentice, reached over the table to touch her hand and slowly said: "You will be a great Custodian one day. But before then you need to practice and master the art of making The Perfect Gift work for you. It will take some months, maybe even a few years, and on many occasions you will neglect to use The Perfect Gift.

"You will forget what it has given you, what it can give you and what it can continue to give you. You will be reminded to use The Perfect Gift when life is going badly and you will, initially, fail to use it to make your life better when it is already going well. But eventually, if you keep working at it, The Perfect Gift will give you mastery of your life.

"When you have demonstrated by your life that you have indeed used The Perfect Gift to its full potential we will contact you and invite you to become a Custodian.

"In the meantime you can contact any of us to ask for guidance in realising the benefits of The Perfect Gift.

"I have one more thing I must ask you to do. Guess what it is?" finished the Sixth Custodian.

"Could it be to write a summary?" asked the recipient of The Perfect Gift.

I am in control of what I achieve,

if I control my behaviour.

I can behave in anyway I want to.

I am in control of my behaviour,

if I control what I feel.

I am in control of what I feel,

if I control what I think.

I can make myself feel anyway I want to.

I am in control of what I think,

if I control what I believe.

I can think anything I like in any way I want to.

I am in control of what I believe,

if I provide sufficient justification for what I choose to believe.

I can choose to believe anything I want to.

I have The Perfect Gift.

I must practice using and harnessing The Perfect Gift.

I must overcome the human tendency to forget that I have The Perfect Gift.

Other books by Nigel MacLennan

Coaching and Mentoring, Gower (Number 1 best-seller)
Opportunity Spotting, Gower (2 editions)
Counselling for Managers, Gower
Awesome Purpose, Gower
Harnessing The Perfect Gift, Aria, will be available soon.

Dr Nigel MacLennan

Is the author of five other books all of which were published by Gower. He is the coach to many of the UK's most successful CEO's and Directors. He has led the Boards of many national and international companies to form their visions, set their strategies, manage their cultures, create new products and services and design their customer service experience. He was Visiting Professor of Management at USE Monaco for nearly a decade, and was the Director of The Chartered Institute of Management responsible for persuading the Board to adopt best practice corporate governance based on his 5th book, Awesome Purpose. He runs MacLennan, a consultancy operating at Board level providing substantial business improvements on a guaranteed results basis. He has led or part led the successful turnaround of four major businesses in the last three years. Nigel relaxes by flying light aircraft and sailing yachts. He can be contacted via:

www.maclennan.~~uk.com~~ biz
or by e-mail: info@maclennan.~~uk.com~~ biz